PAWsome Party

The party was pup-tastic and it's time to head home. **Give Ryder and Zuma some colour.**

Clowning Around

With his fuzzy wig, Mr Porter's clown costume is fun-tastic. **Add lots of bright and bold colours.**

Looking Magical

Cali thinks Katie's witch costume looks wicked. **Make her outfit look magical with colour.**

Costume Cuddles

Chickaletta didn't recognize the Mayor in her ladybird costume. **Give Mayor Goodway and her deputy some colour.**

Cap'n Octopus

Marshall and Zuma think there's something fishy about Cap'n Turbot's costume. **Colour the party picture.**

Super cop

Police pup Chase is always on duty. **Colour his super cop costume, so he looks PAWsome for the party.**

CHASE

Pirate Pet

Meow me hearties! With her eye patch, Cali makes a great pirate's pet. **Give the cat a splash of colour.**

Alex-osaurus

With teeth and a tail, Alex's costume is totally ROAR-some! **Colour in the fancy-dress dinosaur.**

Rocky
The Viking

Rocky's face looks even furrier when he wears his Viking costume. **Add colour to his recycled costume.**

ROCKY

Brave And Strong

The knight in shining armour is saving Wally the walrus. **Give Sir Ryder some heroic colours.**

Pumpkins Might Fly

Skye is giving Marshall a lift to the fancy dress party. **Colour his pumpkin costume bright orange.**

MARSHALL

Pirate Pup

Zuma can't wait for the costume party to start. **Give the pirate pup some swashbuckling colours.**

Princess Skye

Pilot pup Skye looks as pretty as a princess. Colour her costume in shades of pink.

Skye

Rocking Rubble

Dressed as a rock star, Rubble looks totally PAWsome. **Add a pop of colour to his costume.**

RUBBLE

Save the Party

The PAW Patrol has a special mission – to throw the best party in Adventure Bay. **Get the party started by colouring their costumes.**

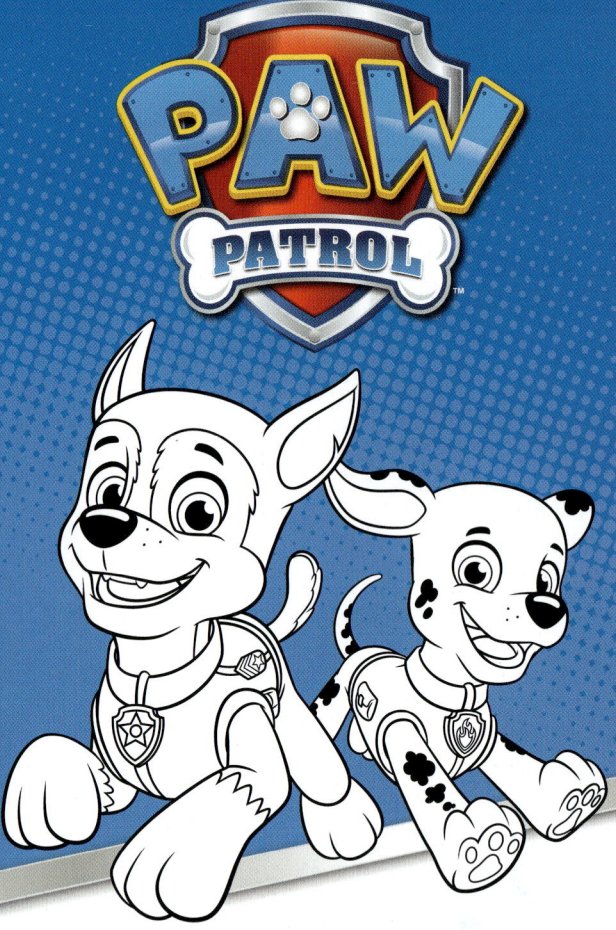

PAW PATROL™: COSTUME PARTY COLOURING
A CENTUM BOOK 9781912707270
Published in Great Britain by Centum Books Ltd
This edition published 2018
1 3 5 7 9 10 8 6 4 2

© 2018 Spin Master PAW Productions Inc. All Rights Reserved. PAW Patrol and all related titles, logos and characters are trademarks of Spin Master Ltd. Nickelodeon and all related titles and logos are trademarks of Viacom International Inc.

All rights reserved. No part of this publication may be reproduced, stored in a retrieval system, or transmitted in any form or by any means, electronic, mechanical, photocopying, recording or otherwise, without the prior permission of the publishers.

Centum Books Ltd, 20 Devon Square, Newton Abbot, Devon TQ12 2HR, UK
books@centumbooksltd.co.uk
CENTUM BOOKS Limited Reg. No. 07641486

A CIP catalogue record for this book is available from the British Library

Printed in China